Bond

Assessment Papers

First papers in
Verbal Reasoning

J M Bond

Text © J M Bond 2007
Original illustrations © Nelson Thornes Ltd 2007

The right of J M Bond to be identified as author of this work has been asserted by
her in accordance with the Copyright, Designs and Patents Act 1988.

First published in 1973 by:
Thomas Nelson and Sons Ltd

This edition published in 2007 by:
Nelson Thornes Ltd
Delta Place
27 Bath Road
CHELTENHAM
GL53 7TH
United Kingdom

10 11 12 / 10 9 8 7

A catalogue record for this book is available from the British Library

ISBN 978 0 7487 8107 2

Page make-up by Tech Set Ltd

Printed in Croatia by Zrinski

Before you get started

What is Bond?

This book is part of the Bond Assessment Papers series for verbal reasoning, which provides a **thorough and continuous course in verbal reasoning** from ages six to twelve. It builds up verbal reasoning skills from book to book over the course of the series.

What does this book cover?

Verbal reasoning questions can be grouped into four distinct groups: sorting words, selecting words, anagrams, coded sequences and logic. This book practises a wide range of questions appropriate to the age group drawn from all these categories. One of the key features of Bond Assessment Papers is that each one practises **a very wide variety of skills and question types** so that children are always challenged to think – and don't get bored repeating the same question type again and again. We believe that variety is the key to effective learning. It helps children 'think on their feet' and cope with the unexpected.

The age given on the cover is for guidance only. As the papers are designed to be reasonably challenging for the age group, any one child may naturally find him or herself working above or below the stated age. The important thing is that children are always encouraged by their performance. Working at the right level is the key to this.

What does the book contain?

- **22 papers** – each one contains 30 questions.
- **Scoring devices** – there are scoring boxes next to the questions and a Progress Chart at the back. The chart is a visual and motivating way for children to see how they are doing. Encouraging them to colour in the chart as they go along and to try to beat their last score can be highly effective!
- **Next Steps** – advice on what to do after finishing the papers can be found on the inside back cover.
- **Answers** – located in an easily-removed central pull-out section. If you lose your answers, please email cservices@nelsonthornes.com for another copy.

How can you use this book?

One of the great strengths of Bond Assessment Papers is their flexibility. They can be used at home, school and by tutors to:

- provide regular verbal reasoning practice in **bite-sized chunks**
- **highlight strengths and weaknesses** in the core skills
- identify **individual needs**
- set **homework**
- set **timed formal practice tests** – allow about 30 minutes.

It is best to start at the beginning and work through the papers in order.

What does a score mean and how can it be improved?

If children colour in the Progress Chart at the back, this will give an idea of how they are doing. The Next Steps inside the back cover will help you to decide what to do next to help a child progress. We suggest that it is always valuable to go over any wrong answers with children.

Don't forget the website…!

Visit www.bond11plus.co.uk for lots of advice, information and suggestions on everything to do with Bond, helping children to do their best, and exams.

Paper 1

1–5 Write the following words in the correct groups.

dog   red   cat   pig   green

Colours

Animals

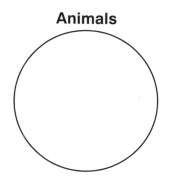

5

Underline the two words which are made from the same letters.

Example	TAP	PET	<u>TEA</u>	POT	<u>EAT</u>
6 ATE	TAR	TEA	ALE	ARE	
7 NAB	BIN	BUN	NOT	NIB	
8 TWO	TOO	TOW	WET	TEN	
9 NET	TON	NUT	NOT	TAN	
10 BAT	BIT	BUT	BET	TUB	

5

Change the first word of the third pair in the same way as the other pairs to give a new word.

Example	bind, hind	bare, hare	but, <u>hut</u>
11 pit, pot	lit, lot	hit _____	
12 hit, hat	sit, sat	pit, _____	
13 bat, bet	sat, set	mat, _____	
14 pen, pan	men, man	fen _____	
15 dig, dog	fig, fog	big, _____	

5

(*1*)

Complete the following sentences by selecting the most sensible word from each group of words given in the brackets. Underline the words selected.

Example The (<u>children</u>, books, foxes) carried the (houses, <u>books</u>, steps) home from the (greengrocer, <u>library</u>, factory).

16 The (house, table, chair) has a (high, tall, big) (garden, doors, curtain).

17 The (dog, baby, kitten) was put in its (bucket, net, pram) ready to be (pushed, chased, rushed) round the park.

18 The (sheep, cow, pig) (barked, crowed, mooed) in the (house, pond, field).

19 The (sky, street, car) was very (delicious, busy, brave).

20 Have you (read, lost, shouted) your (mountain, pen, knee) in the (book, tea, playground)?

5

If the code for TABLE is 1 2 3 4 5, what are the codes for the following words?

21 LET   22 BAT   23 EAT

_____   _____   _____

24 LATE   25 BALE

_____   _____

5

26 Meera is half as old as John. If John is 14, how old is Meera?   _____   I

Look at this weather map and answer the questions.

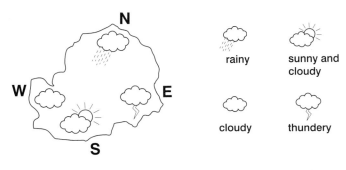

rainy

sunny and cloudy

cloudy

thundery

27 In the north it was _____ .

28 In the south it was _____ .

29 In the west it was _____ .

30 In the east it was _____ .

4

Paper 2

Which one letter can be added to the front of all of these words to make new words?

Example <u>c</u>are   <u>c</u>at   <u>c</u>rate   <u>c</u>all

1 __aste   __ind   __et   __ish

2 __own   __ust   __rag   __ear

3 __ace   __ull   __ind   __ence

4 __ond   __et   __ound   __ie

5 __ang   __at   __link   __ounce

5

Put the words below into alphabetical order.

6 DOG   CAT   COW   BULL

_____ _____ _____ _____

Write the words above backwards in alphabetical order.

7 _____ _____ _____ _____

2

If the code for BREAD is 1 2 3 4 5, what are the codes for the following words?

8 BAR   9 DAD   10 EAR   11 BAD   12 ADD

_____ _____ _____ _____ _____

5

Underline the pair of words most similar in meaning.

Example   come, go   <u>roam, wander</u>   fear, fare

13 break, smash   sand, sea   tea, coffee

14 one, two   brief, short   wet, dry

15 young, old   leg, foot   call, shout

16 green, grass   good, bad   ill, sick

17 tell, story   small, tiny   green, blue

5

Tom is 6. He is three years older than Claire and twice as old as Jack. Gareth is one year older than Jack. Gareth has a twin sister, Morwen. How old is:

18 Claire _____   **19** Jack _____

20 Gareth _____   **21** Morwen _____

Change one word so that the sentence makes sense. Underline the word you are taking out and write your new word on the line.

Example   I waited in line to buy a <u>book</u> to see the film.   *ticket*

22 I slid down the swings in the park.   _____

23 We baked mum's birthday cake in the freezer.   _____

24 The bicycle arrived at the platform on time.   _____

25 Simon put a date on the envelope and posted it.   _____

Underline the one word which **cannot be made** from the letters of the word in capital letters.

Example   S T A T I O N E R Y   stone   ration   <u>nation</u>   noisy

26 STEAK	set	oak	ate	tea
27 CHIPS	ship	hip	sip	fish
28 SNIPE	pen	pea	pin	sip
29 HEART	the	rat	rot	tar
30 WATER	ate	tea	two	tar

Now go to the Progress Chart to record your score!   Total   30

Paper 3

1–4 Underline any words below which have no two letters the same.

AUNT	BABY	NIECE	UNCLE
LION	SHEEP	MOUSE	STOAT

4

Remove one letter from the word in capital letters to leave a new word. The meaning of the new word is given in the clue.

Example   A U N T   an insect   _ant_

5 READ   a colour   _____

6 HOWL   bird   _____

7 CLUB   young lion   _____

8 CAST   an animal   _____

9 THAT   we wear it   _____

5

10 If May 1st is a Thursday what will the date be on Saturday?   _____

11 If Christmas Day is on a Sunday on which day will Boxing Day (the day after Christmas Day) be?   _____

2

Fill in the missing letters. The alphabet has been written out to help you.

A B C D E F G H I J K L M N O P Q R S T U V W X Y Z

Example   AB is to CD as PQ is to _RS_

12 AB is to CD as EF is to   _____

13 B is to D as F is to   _____

14 BA is to DC as FE is to   _____

15 ABC is to DEF as GHI is to   _____

16 A2 is to B3 as C4 is to   _____

5

Underline the word in the brackets closest in meaning to the word in capitals.

Example   UNHAPPY   (unkind   laughter   <u>sad</u>   friendly)

17 GO   (out   leave   come   run)

18 FAST   (quick   slow   stop   speed)

19 WET   (dry   sun   damp   clean)

20 CROSS   (kind   loving   angry   frown)

21 WASH   (clean   face   towel   water)   5

Rearrange the muddled letters in capitals to make a proper word. The answer will complete the sentence sensibly.

Example   A BEZAR is an animal with stripes.   <u>ZEBRA</u>

22 The school SUB was late this morning.   _____

23 It is very OLCD today.   _____

24 Where is your ENP?   _____

25 I have lost my KOBO.   _____

26 What time is the YRATP?   _____   5

Four children are going to do some painting.

A and M use yellow paint.   D and E use orange paint.

A and E paint dogs.   D and M paint cats.

27 Who paints yellow dogs?   ____

28 Who paints orange cats?   ____

29 Who paints orange dogs?   ____

30 Who paints yellow cats?   ____   4

Now go to the Progress Chart to record your score!   Total   30

6

Paper 4

1–5 The first six letters of the alphabet are A B C D E F.

Underline the words below which only contain these letters.

feed	bacon	dice	bead
face	back	bread	deaf
faces	call	deal	fade

5

Change one word so that the sentence makes sense. Underline the word you are taking out and write your new word on the line.

Example   I waited in line to buy a <u>book</u> to see the film.   *ticket*

6 The doctor told the children to sit down and hand in their homework.   _____

7 The mouse wagged its tail because it was happy to get a treat.   _____

8 The car drove over a nail and got a flat windscreen.   _____

9 I make my pillow each morning before I go to school.   _____

10 During the storm the tree lost one of its biggest leaves.   _____

5

Underline the two words, one from each group, which are closest in meaning.

Example   (race, shop, <u>start</u>)   (finish, <u>begin</u>, end)

11 (friend, grin, angry)   (kind, smile, sneeze)

12 (up, over, all)   (down, above, top)

13 (bright, dull, sunny)   (storm, cloudy, rain)

14 (silly, tired, bad)   (child, weary, good)

15 (listen, laugh, cry)   (noisy, hear, row)

5

16 The first lesson at school is at 9 o'clock. If it lasts 30 minutes when will it finish? Underline the correct answer in the brackets.

(09:00, 09:15, 09:30)

17 The last lesson of the day ends at 3:30. If it lasts for one hour, when did it start? Underline the correct answer in brackets.

(2:00, 2:30, 3:00)

2

Remove one letter from the word in capital letters to leave a new word. The meaning of the new word is given in the clue.

Example   A U N T   an insect   *ant*

18 BREAK   a part of a bird   _____

19 BLACK   the opposite of front   _____

20 MICE   frozen water   _____

21 LEAST   the opposite of first   _____

22 PLANE   part of a window   _____   (5)

Complete the following sentences by selecting the most sensible word from each group of words given in the brackets. Underline the words selected.

Example   The (children, books, foxes) carried the (houses, books, steps) home from the (greengrocer, library, factory).

23 My (cat, doll, dog) is wearing a (hard, wooden, spotted) (cup, dish, dress).

24 My (brother, sister, dad) keeps her (book, socks, horse) in the (fridge, road, stable).

25 The (shop, house, pond) closes for (breakfast, lunch, tea).

26 Under the (table, bridge, egg) the (sky, river, castle) was (sleeping, smiling, flowing).

27 Did you (hear, clean, eat) the (chocolate, desk, pencil) that was in the (grass, box, cup)?   (5)

John and Samina like pets. Rita and Mike like football. Mike and John like biking. Samina and Rita like skateboarding.

28 Who likes football and biking?   _____

29 Who likes pets and biking?   _____

30 Who likes skateboarding and football?   _____   (3)

Paper 5

Underline the two words which are the odd ones out in the following groups of words.

Example   black   <u>king</u>   purple   green   <u>house</u>

1 red   blue   egg   green   cup

2 leaf   rose   daisy   flower   poppy

3 number   one   two   many   four

4 hair   friend   sock   shirt   dress

5 glass   jug   table   cup   chair

5

Change the first word into the last word, by changing one letter at a time and making a new, different word in the middle.

Example   TEN   <u>TIN</u>   FIN

6 PIN   _____   WON

7 LIT   _____   HUT

8 BUY   _____   NUT

9 NOW   _____   NET

10 ADD   _____   DID

5

Underline two words, one from each group, that go together to form a new word. The word in the first group always comes first.

Example   (hand, <u>green</u>, for)   (light, <u>house</u>, sure)

11 (race, game, post)   (goal, track, way)

12 (flag, room, stair)   (case, wash, pipe)

2

Rearrange the muddled letters to make words.

13 LELB   14 KEIB   15 HIARC

_____   _____   _____

16 ESNP   17 OKHO

_____   _____

5

If a = 2, b = 3, c = 5, d = 6, find the value of these words.

18 a + b = _____

19 a + b + c = _____

20 d − c = _____

Give the missing number in each sequence.

| **Example** | 2 | 4 | 6 | 8 | <u>10</u> |

21 15	12	9	6	—
22 1	3	—	7	9
23 4	5	6	7	—
24 8	7	—	5	4

If the code for STEAM is 7 5 6 4 8, what are the codes for the following words?

25 MAT _____

26 EAT _____

27 SEA _____

28 AM _____

29 TEA _____

30 MEAT _____

Now go to the Progress Chart to record your score!   Total   30

Paper 6

Underline the pair of words most opposite in meaning.

Example   cup, mug   coffee, milk   <u>hot, cold</u>

1 paper, pen   light, dark   book, read

2 bowl, plate   clear, clean   full, empty

3 wild, cross   under, over   wish, like

4 wet, dry   clip, band   hole, full

5 wing, tail   hard, lump   long, short   ◯ 5

Change the first word of the third pair in the same way as the other pairs to give a new word.

Example   bind, hind   bare, hare   but, <u>hut</u>

6 red, read   led, lead   bed, _____

7 fan, flan   can, clan   pan, _____

8 pop, poop   hop, hoop   lop, _____

9 sad, sand   bad, band   had, _____

10 pit, tip   loop, pool   evil, _____   ◯ 5

The letters SADM are 1 2 3 4 in code. What do these codes stand for?

11 2 1 1   12 1 2 3   13 2 3 3

_____   _____   _____

14 4 2 3   15 3 2 3

_____   _____   ◯ 5

16–18 Underline the words which have their letters in alphabetical order. The alphabet has been written out to help you.

A B C D E F G H I J K L M N O P Q R S T U V W X Y Z

DRAW   BOOT   LOST   SPOT

SOCK   HOST   DARK   LION   ◯ 3

Find the letter which will end the first word and start the second word.

Example   peac (<u>h</u>) ome

19 en (—) ay

20 ar (—) ay

21 si (—) uby

22 li (—) et

23 me (—) wo

5

Give the missing number in the following sequences.

Example   2 4 6 8 <u>10</u>

24	10	9	8	7	—	5
25	50	—	70	80	90	100
26	2	22	3	33	—	44
27	70	—	60	6	50	5

4

If a = 2, b = 3, c = 4, d = 6, find value of:

28 c + d =   _____

29 a + b + c =   _____

30 d − b =   _____

3

Now go to the Progress Chart to record your score!   Total   30

Paper 7

Complete the following sentences by selecting the most sensible word from each group of words given in the brackets. Underline the words selected.

Example The (children, <u>children</u>, foxes) carried the (houses, <u>books</u>, steps) home from the (greengrocer, <u>library</u>, factory).

1 The (dog, cat, horse) was (cross, hungry, sat) and (mewed, shouted, sang) for her food.

2 The (girl, man, women) drove his (car, bus, whisk) to his (home, bed, kitchen).

3 Her (leg, foot, hand) would not (fit, push, wear) the (hat, coat, shoe).

4 He wanted to (paint, sell, run) his (leg, cows, friend) at the (market, zoo, gallery).

5 When are you going to (catch, tidy, win) the (fish, prize, mess) in your (hair, shoe, room)?

5

6–10 Write the following words in the correct groups.

chairs   cat   stool   mouse   pig

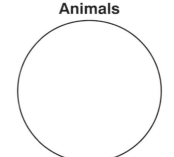

We sit on these   **Animals**

5

Fill in the missing letters and numbers. The alphabet has been written out to help you.

A B C D E F G H I J K L M N O P Q R S T U V W X Y Z

11 A10 is to B8 as C6 is to ____

12 9B is to 8C as 7D is to ____

13 AD is to BE as CF is to ____

14 Z1 is to Y2 as X3 is to ____

15 AZ is to BY as CX is to ____

5

13

Change the first word of the third pair in the same way as the other pairs to give a new word.

Example   bind, hind   bare, hare   but, <u>hut</u>

16 rip, dip   ray, day   rot, _____

17 can, cat   ban, bat   fan, _____

18 fad, fed   bad, bed   lad, _____

19 cot, cat   rot, rat   pot, _____

20 nip, nap   lip, lap   tip, _____

5

Find the letter which will end the first word and start the second word.

Example   peac (<u>h</u>) ome

21 wir (___) nd

22 sno (___) ork

23 nes (___) ime

24 ca (___) wo

25 bu (___) es

5

If a = 1, b = 2, c = 3, d = 5, find the value of:

26 a + b + c = ___

27 d − c =   ___

28 b + c + d = ___

3

Sarah gets three times as much pocket money as Raj got two years ago. Raj's pocket money goes up by £1 a year. He now gets £3 a week.

29 How much did Raj get two years ago?   ___

30 How much does Sarah get?   ___

2

Paper 8

Which one letter can be added to the front of all of these words to make new words?

Example   <u>c</u>are   <u>c</u>at   <u>c</u>rate   <u>c</u>all

1 ___lean   ___ase   ___heap   ___row

2 ___and   ___one   ___end   ___in

3 ___ear   ___hip   ___hen   ___asp

4 ___eat   ___ole   ___ard   ___ouse

5 ___able   ___ray   ___hen   ___an   5

Underline the word in the brackets closest in meaning to the word in capitals.

Example   UNHAPPY   (unkind   laughter   <u>sad</u>   friendly)

6 RULER   (crown   queen   palace   straight)

7 BOY   (child   toddler   lad   baby)

8 BOAT   (sailor   sea   ocean   ship)

9 JUMP   (cross   run   leap   fall)

10 HARD   (easy   difficult   nasty   solid)   5

In each line, underline the word which would come third if the words were placed in alphabetical order.

11 Sanjay   Mike   Rita   Amin   Claire

12 London   Bath   York   Truro   Paris

13 spoon   pencil   knife   scissors   crayon

14 frog   newt   fish   tadpole   beetle

15 mice   nail   tree   apple   zebra   5

15

Complete the following expressions by underlining the missing word.

Example   Frog is to tadpole as swan is to (duckling, baby, <u>cygnet</u>).

16 Grass is to green as snow is to (blue, white, brown).

17 Fire is to red as sea is to (blue, brown, rough).

18 Cat is to kitten as dog is to (poodle, puppy, dog).

19 Water is to drink as bread is to (eat, plate, cup).

20 July is to June as May is to (June, April, March).

Choose the word or phrase that makes each sentence true.

Example   A LIBRARY always has (posters, a carpet, <u>books</u>, DVDs, stairs).

21 A TREE always has (flowers, a bird feeder, berries, roots, leaves).

22 A VILLAGE always has (a petrol station, an airport, houses, a leisure centre, a clothing shop).

23 A TELEVISION always has (a stand, a DVD player, a remote control, a screen, a video recorder).

24 A GARDEN CENTRE always has (a restaurant, books, plants, swing sets, customers).

25 A SANDWICH always has (cheese, lettuce, butter, bread, ham).

Find a word that is similar in meaning to the word in capital letters and that rhymes with the second word.

Example   CABLE   tyre   *wire*

26 RENT   spire   _____

27 FRIEND   late   _____

28 WOOLLY ANIMAL sleep   _____

29 MIDDAY   spoon   _____

30 PIPS   leads   _____

Now go to the Progress Chart to record your score!   Total   30

16

Paper 9

Find a word that can be put in front of each of the following words to make new, compound words.

Example	CAST	FALL	WARD	POUR	_DOWN_
1 CAKE	CUP	POT	ROOM	_____	
2 LID	PATCH	BALL	SIGHT	_____	
3 SHIP	LIGHT	FISH	BURST	_____	
4 LONG	LAMP	ACHE	BAND	_____	
5 CHILD	FATHER	STAND	PARENT	_____	

5

Find a word that is similar in meaning to the word in capital letters and that rhymes with the second word.

Example	CABLE	tyre	_wire_
6 VEHICLE		far	_____
7 A ROAD		meet	_____
8 GROCERIES		mood	_____
9 SPONGE		make	_____

4

Sue and Paul have chips. Colin and Anna have pizza.
Anna and Sue put salt on their food. Paul and Colin put ketchup on their food.

10 Who puts salt on their chips? _____

11 Who puts ketchup on their pizza? _____

12 Who puts ketchup on their chips? _____

13 Who puts salt on their pizza? _____

4

Change one word so that the sentence makes sense. Underline the word you are taking out and write your new word on the line.

Example I waited in line to buy a <u>book</u> to see the film. *ticket*

14 The pilot asked the passengers to stay in their seats because the train was about to take off. _____

15 Lemar put the key in the roof and opened the door to his flat. _____

16 My mum likes a hot cup of tea when she gets up each evening. _____

17 The girls' netball team cheered when they lost the match. _____

18 'Please hurry or we're going to be early for school.' _____ **5**

If the code for MASTER is 9 5 8 6 7 1, what are the codes for the following words?

19 MAT _____

20 TEA _____

21 ARM _____

22 MAR _____

23 RAT _____ **5**

Change the first word into the last word, by changing one letter at a time and making a new, different word in the middle.

Example TEN <u>TIN</u> FIN

24 PUN _____ MAN

25 SON _____ BUN

26 MET _____ MAY

27 MIX _____ FOX

28 POT _____ PEN **5**

Kim is in the drama club which meets on Tuesday and Thursday. She is also in the swimming club which meets on Wednesday. On Monday and Thursday, Kim has piano lessons.

29 On which day does Kim have the most activities? _____

30 On which school day does Kim not have any activities? _____ **2**

Now go to the Progress Chart to record your score! Total **30**

18

Paper 10

Underline the pair of words most similar in meaning.

Example   come, go   <u>roam, wander</u>   fear, fare

1   warm, sunny   good, luck   dark, light

2   long, walk   high, jump   thin, slim

3   middle, centre   rough, dry   weak, strong

4   alley, lane   real, false   back, front

5   awake, asleep   tidy, neat   bake, oven

5

Find the letter which will end the first word and start the second word.

Example   peac (h) ome

6   ad (__) en

7   to (__) lf

8   sa (__) ou

9   fi (__) ew

10   od (__) ad

5

Remove one letter from the word in capital letters to leave a new word. The meaning of the new word is given in the clue.

Example   A U N T   an insect   <u>ant</u>

11   STING   something a pop star can do   _____

12   HAUNT   a relation   _____

13   FLEET   part of our body   _____

14   HOARD   not soft   _____

15   SHOE   a garden tool   _____

5

Complete the following sentences by selecting the most sensible word from each group of words given in the brackets. Underline the words selected.

Example   The (<u>children</u>, books, foxes) carried the (houses, <u>books</u>, steps) home from the (greengrocer, <u>library</u>, factory).

16   The girl (tore, put on, cut) her (overall, dress, apron) and went to the (bath, kitchen, cook).

19

17 The (birds, bees, flowers) needed (sweeping, brushing, watering) as they were very (wet, dry, cold).

18 The (rider, player, walker) kicked the (ground, ball, horse) into the (hole, house, goal).

19 The small (horse, mouse, fly) squeezed into its (bed, hole, trap) and ate the (cheese, spring, fish).

20 The (flock, crowd, team) (ate, stole, scored) three (houses, goals, frogs). ⊂ 5

If the code for CREATE is 5 6 4 8 9 4, what do these codes stand for?

21 589 _____

22 489 _____

23 865 _____

24 948 _____

25 6894 _____ ⊂ 5

In a test of 40 questions there was one mark for each correct answer. Write down the number of marks each person got.

26 C got half right. ___

27 B got 3 more than C. ___

28 D got 2 less than C ___

29 E got 2 less than D. ___

30 A had only 1 mistake. ___ ⊂ 5

Now go to the Progress Chart to record your score! Total ◯ 30

20

Paper 11

Complete the following expressions by underlining in the missing word.

Example   Frog is to tadpole as swan is to (duckling, baby, <u>cygnet</u>).

1 People are to house as car is to (hens, garage, paint).

2 Skip is to rope as cricket is to (stick, bat, net).

3 Cats are to mew as dogs are to (bones, lead, bark).

4 Car is to road as train is to (station, rails, engine).

5 Man is to foot as lion is to (foot, paw, paddle).

⬤ 5

Which one letter can be added to the front of all of these words to make new words?

Example   <u>c</u>are   <u>c</u>at   <u>c</u>rate   <u>c</u>all

6 __late   __an   __op   __lane

7 __lag   __ool   __ig   __lower

8 __ing   __heel   __ipe   __ater

9 __lad   __low   __rip   __un

10 __all   __ank   __ime   __ower

⬤ 5

Change one word so that the sentence makes sense. Underline the word you are taking out and write your new word on the line.

Example   I waited in line to buy a <u>book</u> to see the film.   *ticket*

11 Turn the lamp on. It's light in here!   _____

12 It was so cold, Mia lit the fan to keep warm.   _____

13 The rain blew the leaves off the trees.   _____

14 The airline pilot sailed over the sea in his plane.   _____

⬤ 4

Underline the one word which **cannot be made** from the letters of the word in capital letters.

Example   S T A T I O N E R Y   stone   ration   <u>nation</u>   noisy

15 CLOSED   sold   cold   dose   seed

16 CHARGE   gear   have   cage   race

17 FRIEND   fired   fend   deaf   find

18 OLIVES   live   vest   sole   lies

19 INVENTS   nine   nest   even   vine

     5

20 My watch is 5 minutes slow and it shows 12:30.

    What is the right time?   _____

21 If I had 20p more I would have twice as much as my sister who has 50p.

    How much have I now?   _____

     2

Fill in the missing numbers and letters in each sequence.

Example   2   4   6   8   <u>10</u>

22   33   30   ___   24   21   18

23   A9   B8   C7   ___   E5   F4

24   6   11   16   ___   26   31

25   3   7   11   15   19   ___

     4

Underline the word in the brackets closest in meaning to the word in capitals.

Example   UNHAPPY   (unkind   laughter   <u>sad</u>   friendly)

26 CLEVER   (teacher   school   bright   dull)

27 STORY   (tale   read   book   paper)

28 MEAL   (table   chair   dinner   eat)

29 ALWAYS   (never   sometimes   hour   forever)

30 END   (start   finish   race   entry)

     5

Paper 1

1–5 *Colours:* red, green
     Animals: dog, cat, pig
  6 ATE, TEA
  7 BIN, NIB
  8 TWO, TOW
  9 TON, NOT
 10 BUT, TUB
 11 hot
 12 pat
 13 met
 14 fan
 15 bog
 16 house, big, garden
 17 baby, pram, pushed
 18 cow, mooed, field
 19 street, busy
 20 lost, pen, playground
 21 451
 22 321
 23 521
 24 4215
 25 3245
 26 7
 27 rainy
 28 sunny and cloudy
 29 cloudy
 30 thundery

Paper 2

  1 w
  2 d
  3 f
  4 p
  5 b
  6 BULL, CAT, COW, DOG
  7 GOD, LLUB, TAC, WOC
  8 142
  9 545
 10 342
 11 145
 12 455
 13 break, smash
 14 brief, short
 15 call, shout
 16 ill, sick
 17 small, tiny
 18 3
 19 3
 20 4
 21 4
 22 swings, slide
 23 freezer, oven
 24 bicycle, train
 25 date, stamp
 26 oak
 27 fish
 28 pea
 29 rot
 30 two

Paper 3

  1 AUNT
  2 UNCLE
  3 LION
  4 MOUSE
  5 red
  6 owl
  7 cub
  8 cat
  9 hat
 10 May 3rd
 11 Monday
 12 GH
 13 H
 14 HG
 15 JKL
 16 D5
 17 leave
 18 quick
 19 damp
 20 angry
 21 clean
 22 BUS
 23 COLD
 24 PEN
 25 BOOK
 26 PARTY
 27 A
 28 D
 29 E
 30 M

Paper 4

1–5 feed, bead, face, deaf, fade
6 doctor, teacher
7 mouse, dog
8 windscreen, tyre
9 pillow, bed
10 leaves, branches
11 grin, smile
12 over, above
13 dull, cloudy
14 tired, weary
15 listen, hear
16 09:30
17 2:30
18 beak
19 back
20 ice
21 last
22 pane
23 doll, spotted, dress
24 sister, horse, stable
25 shop, lunch
26 bridge, river, flowing
27 eat, chocolate, box
28 Mike
29 John
30 Rita

Paper 5

1 egg, cup
2 leaf, flower
3 number, many
4 hair, friend
5 table, chair
6 WIN
7 HIT
8 BUT
9 NEW
10 AID
11 racetrack
12 staircase
13 BELL
14 BIKE
15 CHAIR
16 PENS
17 HOOK
18 5
19 10
20 1
21 3
22 5
23 8
24 6
25 845
26 645
27 764
28 48
29 564
30 8645

Paper 6

1 light, dark
2 full, empty
3 under, over
4 wet, dry
5 long, short
6 bead
7 plan
8 loop
9 hand
10 live
11 ASS
12 SAD
13 ADD
14 MAD
15 DAD
16–18 BOOT, LOST, HOST
19 d
20 m
21 r
22 p
23 t
24 6
25 60
26 4
27 7
28 10
29 9
30 3

Paper 7

1 cat, hungry, mewed
2 man, car, home
3 foot, fit, shoe
4 sell, cows, market
5 tidy, mess, room
6–10 *We sit on these:* chairs, stool
    Animals: cat, mouse, pig
11 D4
12 6E
13 DG
14 W4
15 DW
16 dot
17 fat
18 led
19 pat
20 tap
21 e
22 w
23 t
24 t
25 y
26 6
27 2
28 10
29 £1
30 £3

Paper 8

1 c
2 b
3 w
4 h
5 t
6 queen
7 lad
8 ship
9 leap
10 difficult
11 Mike
12 Paris
13 pencil
14 frog
15 nail
16 white
17 blue
18 puppy
19 eat
20 April
21 roots
22 houses
23 a screen
24 plants
25 bread
26 hire
27 mate
28 sheep
29 noon
30 seeds

Paper 9

1 TEA
2 EYE
3 STAR
4 HEAD
5 GRAND
6 car
7 street
8 food
9 cake
10 Sue
11 Colin
12 Paul
13 Anna
14 train, plane
15 roof, lock
16 evening, morning
17 lost, won
18 early, late
19 956
20 675
21 519
22 951
23 156
24 PAN
25 SUN
26 MAT
27 FIX
28 PET
29 Thursday
30 Friday

Paper 10

1 warm, sunny
2 thin, slim
3 middle, centre
4 alley, lane
5 tidy, neat
6 d
7 e
8 y
9 n
10 d
11 sing
12 aunt
13 feet
14 hard
15 hoe
16 put on, apron, kitchen
17 flowers, watering, dry
18 player, ball, goal
19 mouse, hole, cheese
20 team, scored, goals
21 CAT
22 EAT
23 ARC
24 TEA
25 RATE
26 20
27 23
28 18
29 16
30 39

Paper 11

1 garage
2 bat
3 bark
4 rails
5 paw
6 p
7 f
8 w
9 g
10 t
11 light, dark
12 fan, fire
13 rain, wind
14 sailed, flew
15 seed
16 have
17 deaf
18 vest
19 even
20 12:35
21 80p
22 27
23 D6
24 21
25 23
26 bright
27 tale
28 dinner
29 forever
30 finish

Paper 12

1 A
2 J
3 M
4 P
5 girl
6 morning
7 go
8 double
9 cold
10 burgle, steal
11 truck, lorry
12 talk, chat
13 start, begin
14 quick, fast
15 tame
16 heat
17 host
18 cheap
19 black
20 13
21 £1
22 ARM, RAM
23 LOW, OWL
24 WON, NOW
25 CAR, ARC
26 DAB, BAD
27 C6
28 24
29 6
30 ae

Paper 13

1. Geoffrey
2. 18th December
3. November
4. WIN
5. HIT
6. BUT
7. RIB
8. HAT
9. wide, broad
10. shut, closed
11. gift, present
12. tall, high
13. peaceful, calm
14. 465
15. 536
16. 624
17. 2653
18. 5362
19. CAT
20. FISH
21. DOG
22. MEAT
23. BARKS
24. sat, mended, bike
25. cold, blowing, outside
26. played, game, computer
27. swimmer, dived, pool
28. clock, ticked, shelf
29. car
30. pudding

Paper 14

1. Tom
2. Leo
3. 5, 2, 1, 3, 4
4. 1, 3, 5, 2, 4
5. 3, 1, 2, 5, 4
6. 3, 2, 1, 4, 5
7. sad, sorry
8. neat, tidy
9. laugh, chuckle
10. glad, happy
11. above, over
12. 533
13. 253
14. 265
15. 3654
16. 35462
17. trace
18. told
19. trade
20. comet
21. health
22. pasta, water
23. parade, street
24. homework, his
25. shoes, two
26. fun
27. dot
28. set
29. nut
30. ace

Paper 15

1–5 *Vegetables:* leeks, peas
Colours: yellow, brown, pink
6. DOG
7. LAMB
8. PONY
9. GOAT
10. CAT
11. lock
12. each
13. old
14. ears
15. nets
16. book
17. game
18. school
19. car
20. seagull
21. DEED
22. FACED
23. DEAF
24. FEED
25. 2
26. 6
27. 13
28. train, catch
29. tree, wind
30. final, goal

Paper 16

1. tint
2. chat
3. west
4. beat
5. ears
6. m
7. t
8. k
9. f
10. h
11. sand
12. link
13. bake
14. hoot
15. pan
16. read, magazine, bed
17. enjoyed, colourful, fireworks
18. left, clothes, bathroom
19. boat, tossed, sea
20. horses, neighed, stable
21. 18
22. 21
23. 2
24. 3
25. 8
26. seagull
27. fairground
28. flagpole
29. network
30. paintbox

Paper 17

1. mane
2. pen
3. tall
4. wall
5. and
6. story
7. stride
8. shatter
9. journey
10. uproar
11. soft
12. tame
13. lost
14. loud
15. e
16. s
17. w
18. t
19. t
20. c
21. a
22. c
23. 9531
24. 5981
25. 13538
26. SET
27. TAN
28. Robin
29. Megan
30. Mark

Paper 18

1. r
2. p
3. s
4. h
5. d
6. bike, track
7. the, into
8. harness, dog
9. cold, fingers
10. water, sea
11. stool, chair
12. paper, rubber
13. house, cottage
14. sea, ocean
15. 12
16. 123
17. 423
18. 325
19. 1236
20. t
21. l
22. d
23. l
24. r
25. m
26. l
27. d
28. g
29. h
30. e

Paper 19

1 d
2 l
3 n
4 f
5 w
6 chair, floral, material
7 pictures, walls, room
8 ever, sea, dolphins
9 dragon, scales, back
10 squeezed, gate, quickly
11 jungle, zoo
12 foot, hand
13 blunt, sharp
14 wear
15 rest
16 near
17 wasp
18 hens
19 lamp
20 read
21 frog
22 nest
23 mast
24 shut
25 lamb
26 hand
27 small
28 out
29 2, 1, 3, 5, 4
30 5, 3, 2, 1, 4

Paper 20

1 hound
2 fight
3 start
4 mouse
5 crate
6 t
7 t
8 g
9 p
10 d
11 bat
12 pain
13 harp
14 race
15 bear
16 weak
17 ill
18 low
19 hot
20 last
21 Q
22 LEAD
23 DAME
24 D
25 Friday
26 Wednesday
27 SEA
28 LIFE
29 BLACK
30 BATTLE

Paper 21

1

R	A	T
A	G	O
M	A	P

2

B	I	N
A	C	E
G	E	T

3 blind
4 coast
5 slow
6 bald
7 learn
8 IDC
9 FHI
10 DFH
11 FHAC
12 IDCHA
13–17 *Vegetables (A)*: leeks, onions
Buildings (B): house, school
Things we do (C): cycle, run, write
Birds (D): owl, lark, swan
(give one mark for each two correct)
18 WHEN
19 FLYING
20 INDIA
21 QUICK
22 CINEMA
23 bag, DVDs, library
24 touch, fence, electric
25 sea, crashing, shore
26 gobbled, pudding, greedily
27 postman, parcel
28 Thursday
29 12:25
30 15th

Paper 22

1 d
2 n
3 t
4 l
5 n
6 jawbone
7 bagpipes
8 drawbridge
9 feast
10 frail
11 plant
12 plate
13 slip
14 speak
15 fright
16 teach
17 scratch
18 stream
19 train
20 coast
21 cat
22 sea
23 car
24 hen
25 water
26 BXQ
27 PXQ
28 LPF
29 GEAR
30 RANG

Paper 12

A and M were tall. J and P were short. M and J were fair and A and P were dark.

1 Who was tall and dark? _____

2 Who was short and fair? _____

3 Who was tall and fair? _____

4 Who was short and dark? _____

⬤ 4

Complete the following expressions by underlining the missing word.

Example Frog is to tadpole as swan is to (duckling, baby, <u>cygnet</u>).

5 Man is to woman as boy is to (child, son, girl).

6 Night is to day as evening is to (lunch, morning, sunset).

7 Red is to stop as green is to (danger, go, wait).

8 One is to single as two is to (three, double, mix).

9 Oven is to hot as refrigerator is to (shelf, food, cold).

⬤ 5

Underline the two words in each line which are most similar in type or meaning.

Example <u>dear</u> pleasant poor extravagant <u>expensive</u>

10 rough burgle even steal hungry

11 truck car train lorry bike

12 talk listen put aunt chat

13 start close late stop begin

14 quick slow steady fast walk

⬤ 5

Change the first word of the third pair in the same way as the other pairs to give a new word.

Example bind, hind   bare, hare   but, <u>hut</u>

15 some, same   dome, dame   tome, ⎯⎯⎯

16 four, hour   fang, hang   feat, ⎯⎯⎯

17 lair, hair   lint, hint   lost, ⎯⎯⎯

18 clan, clean   dram, dream   chap, ⎯⎯⎯

19 pace, place   sing, sling   back, ⎯⎯⎯   ◯ 5

20 In 3 years time Shen will be twice as old as I am now. If I am 8 now how old is Shen?   ⎯

21 If I had 20p more I would have twice as much as my sister who has 60p. How much have I?   ⎯   ◯ 2

Underline the two words which are made from the same letters.

Example TAP PET <u>TEA</u> POT <u>EAT</u>

22 ARM   RIM   AIR   RUM   RAM

23 PIT   LOW   PET   OWL   LET

24 WON   OUT   NOW   WIN   HIM

25 BUS   CAR   ARK   FOX   ARC

26 MAN   CUT   DAB   DIM   BAD   ◯ 5

Fill in the missing numbers and letters in each sequence.

Example 2 4 6 8 <u>10</u>

27 A10   B8   ⎯   D4   E2   F0

28 28   ⎯   20   16   12   8

29 3   ⎯   9   12   15   18

30 ab   ac   ad   ⎯   af   ag   ◯ 4

Paper 13

My brother's name begins with the 7th letter of the alphabet.

1 Is it Francis, Henry or Geoffrey? _____

2 His birthday is exactly a week before Christmas Day.

Is it the 16th, 17th or 18th December? _____

3 My birthday is in the month beginning with the 14th letter
of the alphabet.

Is it in October, November or March? _____

3

Change the first word into the last word, by changing one letter at a time and
making a new, different word in the middle.

Example   TEN   TIN   FIN

4 PIN _____ WON

5 LIT _____ HUT

6 BUY _____ NUT

7 RUB _____ BIB

8 HAY _____ PAT

5

Underline the two words, one from each group, which are closest in meaning.

Example ,   (race, shop, <u>start</u>)   (finish, <u>begin</u>, end)

9 (large, slow, wide)   (broad, quick, small)

10 (sound, shut, people)   (call, closed, open)

11 (away, gift, begin)   (present, there, play)

12 (shape, size, tall)   (long, high, small)

13 (temper, cross, peaceful)   (rough, calm, storm)

5

If the code for MATTER is 4 6 5 5 3 2, what are the codes for the following words?

14 MAT _____   **15** TEA _____   **16** ARM _____

17 RATE _____   **18** TEAR _____

19–23 Rearrange the muddled words in capital letters so that each sentence makes sense.

     Example   There are sixty SNODCES <u>SECONDS</u> in a UTMINE <u>MINUTE</u>.

     My TAC _____ loves SHIF _____ but my ODG _____ likes

     TEAM _____. He SKBRA _____ when he is hungry.

Complete the following sentences by selecting the most sensible word from each group of words given in the brackets. Underline the words selected.

     Example   The (<u>children</u>, books, foxes) carried the (houses, <u>books</u>, steps) home from the (greengrocer, <u>library</u>, factory).

24 The boy (swam, slept, sat) and (burnt, cut, mended) his (knee, bike, dog).

25 There's a (blue, cold, purple) wind (walking, blowing, hooting) (inside, outside, between).

26 Have you (played, clicked, win) the (board, friend, game) on the (film, computer, kitchen)?

27 The (fish, swimmer, boat) (dived, surfed, fished) into the (net, pool, bath).

28 The (clock, cat, fridge) (cooked, hummed, ticked) on the (light, fire, shelf).

If these words were placed in alphabetical order, which word would come 4th?

	Example	anxiety	auction	ancient	axiomatic	<u>auxiliary</u>
29	cow	car	bee	boar	apple	_____
30	house	pudding	hamster	pie	quarter	_____

Paper 14

Tom is smaller than Kang and Kang is smaller than Leo.

1 Who is the smallest? _____

2 Who is the biggest? _____

2

Number the words in each line in alphabetical order.

3 bun __ bed __ bat __ big __ bog __

4 sat __ sit __ such __ set __ slide __

5 dig __ dad __ desk __ dull __ do __

6 fig __ feel __ far __ for __ full __

4

Underline the pair of words most similar in meaning.

Example come, go roam, wander fear, fare

7 bottom, top sand, stones sad, sorry

8 play, work neat, tidy day, week

9 laugh, chuckle good, bad price, cheap

10 few, many glad, happy over, under

11 above, over hard, soft up, down

5

If the code for READS is 4 6 5 3 2, what are the codes for the following words?

12 ADD _____

13 SAD _____

14 SEA _____

15 DEAR _____

16 DARES _____

5

Underline the one word which **cannot be made** from the letters of the word in capital letters.

Example   S T A T I O N E R Y   stone   ration   <u>nation</u>   noisy

17 SWEATER   tease   wart   trace   sweet

18 RELATION   tale   told   ration   late

19 CUSTARD   star   crust   trade   stud

20 COMRADE   dear   comet   dram   raced

21 WEATHER   health   wet   thaw   tree

Find and underline the two words which need to change places for each sentence to make sense.

Example   She went to <u>letter</u> the <u>write</u>.

22 Make sure the pasta is boiling before you put the water in.

23 The police closed off the parade for the street.

24 Nick needed to use the computer to do homework his.

25 Catrin couldn't stop laughing when she saw that she was wearing shoes different two.

Change the first word of the third pair in the same way as the other pairs to give a new word.

Example   bind, hind   bare, hare   but, <u>hut</u>

26 ran, run   ban, bun   fan, _____

27 no, not   go, got   do, _____

28 pat, pet   bat, bet   sat, _____

29 cot, cut   pot, put   not, _____

30 rice, ice   pink, ink   face, _____

1–5 Write the following words in the correct groups.

yellow   leeks   brown   pink   peas

Vegetables   **Colours**

5

Rearrange the muddled words in capital letters to make sense. They are all animals.

6 OGD   _____

7 BLMA   _____

8 PYON   _____

9 OATG   _____

10 ACT   _____

5

Remove one letter from the word in capital letters to leave a new word. The meaning of the new word is given in the clue.

Example   A U N T   an insect   <u>ant</u>

11 CLOCK   you use a key in this   _____

12 PEACH   every one   _____

13 BOLD   opposite of young   _____

14 YEARS   we hear with these   _____

15 NESTS   fishermen use them   _____

5

Underline the word in the brackets which goes best with the words given outside the brackets.

Example word, paragraph, sentence (pen, cap, <u>letter</u>, top, stop)

16 page, cover, words (television, book, poster, flower, photo)

17 board, dice, rules (match, swim, laws, tired, game)

18 teacher, pupil, classroom (bed, artist, school, shop, tree)

19 bus, truck, train (car, chair, road, boxes, conductor)

20 robin, pigeon, magpie (squirrel, seagull, mouse, snake, mole) ⟨5⟩

The first six letters of the alphabet are A B C D E F.

Take these letters out of the following words, then underline the words that would completely disappear.

Example LOST SHOE <u>BEAD</u> NEAT

21 DREAM CRAFT DEED IDEAL

22 FLOOD FACED FIRE FEET

23 DEAR DREAD AFTER DEAF

24 FEED CREED CREAM FATED ⟨4⟩

If a = 3, b = 4, c = 6, e = 9, find the value of:

25 c − b = _____

26 e − a = _____

27 a + b + c = _____ ⟨3⟩

Find and underline the two words which need to change places for each sentence to make sense.

Example She went to <u>letter</u> the <u>write</u>.

28 Lola ran to train the catch.

29 The tree blew the wind over.

30 He scored the final in the goal minute. ⟨3⟩

Find the four-letter word hidden at the end of one word and the beginning of the next word. The order of the letters may not be changed.

Example   The children had bats and balls.   _sand_

1 The game went into extra time.   _____

2 They left the sandy beach at five o'clock.   _____

3 We stayed at the hotel by the sea.   _____

4 We had to be at the station by six.   _____

5 One bear strayed out of the cave.   _____   **5**

Find the letter which willl end the first word and start the second word.

Example   peac (h) ome

6 the (__) any

7 fas (__) hin

8 cas (__) nee

9 hal (__) ish

10 bat (__) ard   **5**

Remove one letter from the word in capital letters to leave a new word. The meaning of the new word is given in the clue.

Example   A U N T   an insect   _ant_

11 STAND   it is on the beach   _____

12 BLINK   a piece in a chain   _____

13 BRAKE   to cook a cake   _____

14 SHOOT   to make a noise   _____

15 PANE   we use it when cooking   _____   **5**

Complete the following sentences by selecting the most sensible word from each group of words given in the brackets. Underline the words selected.

> **Example** The (children, books, foxes) carried the (houses, books, steps) home from the (greengrocer, library, factory).

16 Dad (drank, read, cooked) the (cushion, magazine, chair) before he went to (bed, the river, storm).

17 Ruby (scared, enjoyed, wished) the (colourful, squib, sparkle) display of (swimming, fireworks, bonfire).

18 Why have you (left, planted, lost) your (friends, clothes, holidays) in the (sunshine, fridge, bathroom)?

19 The (boat, ships, cabin) was (washed, tossed, hurl) about on the stormy (wave, sea, beach).

20 The (cats, dogs, horses) (mooed, neighed, grunted) to be let out of their (kennel, stable, basket).

5

If a = 4, b = 6, c = 9, d = 12, find the value of:

21 3a + b = _____

22 c + d = _____

23 d − a − b = _____

24 c − b = _____

25 a + a = _____

5

Underline two words, one from each group, that go together to form a new word. The word in the first group always comes first.

> **Example** (hand, green, for)   (light, house, sure)

26 (sky, sea, bird)   (cloud, sand, gull)

27 (fair, light, ride)   (star, ground, train)

28 (hose, sink, flag)   (band, tap, pole)

29 (net, fish, cross)   (work, rod, catch)

30 (draw, colour, paint)   (box, hand, sew)

5

Paper 17

Change the first word of the third pair in the same way as the other pairs to give a new word.

Example   bind, hind   bare, hare   but, <u>hut</u>

1 wan, wane   ban, bane   man, _____

2 man, men   fan, fen   pan, _____

3 bell, ball   cell, call   tell, _____

4 fill, fall   hill, hall   will, _____

5 pill, ill   done, one   sand, _____

5

Underline the word in the brackets closest in meaning to the word in capitals.

Example   UNHAPPY   (unkind   laughter   <u>sad</u>   friendly)

6 TALE   (read   paper   news   story)

7 WALK   (cycle   skate   stride   run)

8 BREAK   (tear   bend   dent   shatter)

9 TRAVEL   (foreign   places   journey   plane)

10 NOISE   (uproar   crowd   hush   end)

5

Underline one word in the brackets which is most opposite in meaning to the word in capitals.

Example   WIDE (broad   long   <u>narrow</u>   motorway)

11 HARD   (work   soft   sharp   tough)

12 WILD   (scary   fierce   tame   find)

13 FOUND   (try   lost   seek   missed)

14 QUIET   (bang   silent   hear   loud)

4

Find the letter which will end the first word and start the second word.

Example   peac (h) ome

15 tre (—) ven

16 mes (—) ent

17 sto (—) ood

18 firs (—) op

19 spli (—) rip

5

If a = 2, b = 3, c = 5, d = 10, give the answer to these calculations as letters.

20 a + b = _____

21 c − b = _____

22 d − c = _____

3

If the code for STANCE is 1 3 5 7 9 8, what are the codes for the following words?

23 CATS   _____

24 ACES   _____

25 STATE   _____

What do these codes stand for?

26 1 8 3   _____

27 3 5 7   _____

5

Megan and Yan like salad. Robin and Mark like pasta, Mark and Megan like apple pie. Yan and Robin like pizza

28 Who like pasta and pizza?   _____

29 Who likes salad and apple pie?   _____

30 Who likes pasta and apple pie?   _____

3

Now go to the Progress Chart to record your score!   Total **30**

34

Paper 18

Which one letter can be added to the front of all of these words to make new words?

Example $\underline{c}$are $\underline{c}$at $\underline{c}$rate $\underline{c}$all

1 __ot   __ake   __eal   __abbit

2 __late   __ill   __ie   __uff

3 __mell   __ail   __ky   __kin

4 __eat   __at   __igh   __ouse

5 __ig   __rain   __ive   __en

5

Find and underline the two words which need to change places for each sentence to make sense.

Example   She went to <u>letter</u> the <u>write</u>.

6 Ethan raced round the bike on his track.

7 The balloon floated the into sky.

8 The guide harness wore a yellow dog.

9 Her cold tingled with the fingers.

4

Underline the two words which are the odd ones out in the following groups of words.

Example   black   <u>king</u>   purple   green   <u>house</u>

10 sob   wail   water   sea   cry

11 mug   stool   beaker   cup   chair

12 pen   paper   pencil   rubber   crayon

13 house   field   meadow   cottage   pasture

14 boat   ship   sea   canoe   ocean

5

These words have been written in code, but the codes are not under the correct words.

TO	TOY	BOY	YOU	TOYS
325	1236	123	423	12

Write the codes under the correct words.

15 TO   **16** TOY   **17** BOY   **18** YOU   **19** TOYS

_____   _____   _____   _____   _____

5

Find the letter which will end the first word and start the second word.

Example   peac (h) ome

20 ten (__) urn   **21** mea (__) oan

22 sen (__) ate   **23** pul (__) ady

24 pai (__) oar   **25** al (__) eat

26 bel (__) aw   **27** len (__) rum

8

If $e = 2$, $f = 4$, $g = 6$, $h = 8$, give the answer to these calculations as letters.

28 $e + f =$ _____

29 $f + f =$ _____

30 $h - g =$ _____

3

Now go to the Progress Chart to record your score!   Total **30**

36

Paper 19

Find the letter which will end the first word and start the second.

Example   peac (<u>h</u>) ome

1 car (__) ive   2 fal (__) awn

3 pla (__) ice   4 cuf (__) air

5 se (__) and

5

Complete the following sentences by selecting the most sensible word from each group of words given in the brackets. Underline the words selected.

Example   The (<u>children</u>, books, foxes) carried the (houses, <u>books</u>, steps) home from the (greengrocer, <u>library</u>, factory).

6 The (cup, chair, fork) is covered with (tall, floral, wide) (sacking, pattern, material).

7 We have three (dogs, pictures, cups) hanging on the (ceiling, lights, walls) of the (garage, shed, room).

8 Did you (always, ever, rare) swim in the (lake, pond, sea) with (boat, dolphins, ocean)?

9 The (pig, dragon, frog) had (babies, stones, scales) on its (back, teeth, cave).

10 Sean (squeezed, jumped, ran) under the (dog, road, gate) as (lazily, sadly, quickly) as he could.

5

Change one word so that the sentence makes sense. Underline the word you are taking out and write your new word on the line.

Example   I waited in line to buy a <u>book</u> to see the film.   *ticket*

11 Dad and I went to see the penguins and monkeys at the local jungle.   _____

12 Michael has broken the fingers and thumb of his left foot.   _____

13 The knife is very blunt so be careful you don't cut yourself.   _____

3

Find the four-letter word hidden at the end of one word and the beginning of the next word. The order of the letters may not be changed.

Example The children had bats and balls. _sand_

14 We are going to the park later. _____

15 Are there steps to climb? _____

16 The baby wasn't born early. _____

17 Ravi was playing with his brother. _____

18 When shall we leave for our holiday? _____   ⬤ 5

Add one letter to the word in capital letters to make a new word. The meaning of the new word is given in the clue.

Example PLAN simple _plain_

19 LAP It is a kind of light. _____

20 RED We are taught to do this at school. _____

21 FOG A tadpole becomes this. _____

22 NET Birds live in it. _____

23 MAT It is part of a ship. _____   ⬤ 5

Complete the following expressions by underlining the missing word.

Example Frog is to tadpole as swan is to (duckling, baby, <u>cygnet</u>).

24 Cheap is to expensive as open is to (money, shop, shut).

25 Cat is to kitten as sheep is to (wool, lamb, pup).

26 Hat is to head as glove is to (foot, leg, hand).

27 Big is to little as large is to (small, huge, enormous).

28 Go is to come as in is to (by, out, road).   ⬤ 5

Number the words in each line in alphabetical order.

29 met __ mat __ mit __ muck __ mock __

30 tug __ tip __ tell __ tall __ top __   ⬤ 2

Paper 20

Find a word that is similar in meaning to the word in capital letters and that rhymes with the second word.

	Example	CABLE	tyre	_wire_
1	A DOG		sound	_____
2	A QUARREL		light	_____
3	TO BEGIN		chart	_____
4	A SMALL RODENT		house	_____
5	A BOX		plate	_____

5

Find the letter that will end the first word and start the second word.

Example   peac (h) ome

6 ben (___) ea

7 boa (___) en

8 son (___) one

9 ram (___) ilot

10 see (___) rip

5

Remove one letter from the word in capital letters to leave a new word. The meaning of the new word is given in the clue.

	Example	A U N T	an insect	_ant_
11	BEAT	you use it to hit a ball	_____
12	PLAIN	a throb, an ache	_____
13	SHARP	a musical instrument	_____
14	TRACE	you run in one of these	_____
15	BLEAR	an animal	_____

5

Underline one word in the brackets which is most opposite in meaning to the word in capitals.

Example   WIDE   (broad   long   <u>narrow</u>   motorway)

16 STRONG   (weak   hard   solid   light)

17 WELL   (water   happy   ill   fit)

18 HIGH   (wide   bottom   low   top)

19 COLD   (chill   hot   warm   boil)

20 FIRST   (last   front   back   lose)

5

Answer these questions. The alphabet has been given to help you.

A B C D E F G H I J K L M N O P Q R S T U V W X Y Z

21 Which letter is as many places after L as H is after C?   —

22 Make a word from the 12th, 5th, 1st and 4th letters.   _____

23 Make a word from the 4th, 1st, 13th and 5th letters.   _____

24 Which letter is as many places from the beginning as W is from the end?   —

4

25 Today is Wednesday 30th December.

On which day will the New Year start?   _____

26 Yesterday was Monday 23rd December.

Christmas Day will be on which day?   _____

2

Find a word that can be put in front of each of the following words to make new, compound words.

Example   CAST   FALL   WARD   POUR   <u>DOWN</u>

27 BIRD   FOOD   FRONT   BED   _____

28 BOAT   TIME   BELT   LIKE   _____

29 BERRY   OUT   BIRD   MAIL   _____

30 DRESS   SHIP   AXE   FIELD   _____

4

Fill in the crosswords so that all the given words are included. You have been given one letter as a clue in each crossword.

1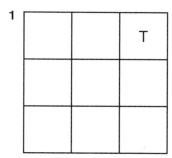

ago, map, rat, aga,
top, ram

2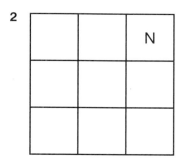

ace, get, bin, net,
bag, ice

2

Add one letter to the word in capital letters to make a new word. The meaning of the new word is given in the clue.

Example   PLAN   simple   _plain_

3 BIND   unable to see   _____

4 COST   on the beach   _____

5 SOW   not as fast   _____

6 BAD   having no hair   _____

7 EARN   understand how to do things   _____

5

If the code for STORED is A C D F H I, what are the codes for the following words?

8 DOT _____   9 RED _____   10 ORE _____

11 REST _____   12 DOTES _____

5

13–17 Look at these groups of words.

A   B   C   D
Vegetables   Buildings   Things we do   Birds

Choose the correct group for each of the words below. Write in the letter.

house ___   owl ___   cycle ___   run ___   write ___

lark ___   onions ___   swan ___   school ___   leeks ___

5

Rearrange the muddled words in capital letters so that each sentence makes sense.

Example   There are sixty SNODCES <u>SECONDS</u> in a UTMINE <u>MINUTE</u>.

18–20 NHEW _____ are you GNLFYI _____ to DANII _____?

21–22 Be CIUKQ _____ or you will be late for the AMINCE _____.

Complete the following sentences by selecting the most sensible word from each group of words given in the brackets. Underline the words selected.

Example   The (<u>children</u>, books, foxes) carried the (houses, <u>books</u>, steps) home from the (greengrocer, <u>library</u>, factory).

23 Ali gets out his (cot, bag, box) to return his (sweets, DVDs, drinks) to the (library, theatre, surgery).

24 Don't (drop, throw, touch) the (wall, book, fence). It is (lost, small, electric).

25 The (grass, cloud, sea) was (rushing, waving, crashing) on the (floor, road, shore).

26 He (gobbled, pushed, stole) the (tower, pudding, door) (badly, sadly, greedily).

27 The (teacher, postman, violinist) brought Anna a (parcel, music, drink) for her birthday.

5

28 If April 1st was a Friday, what day was the 31st March? _____

29 My watch is 5 minutes fast. If my watch shows it is 12.30, what is the real time? _____

30 My birthday is on the 12th. John's birthday is four days after Ranvir's. Ranvir's birthday is the day before mine. What is the date of John's birthday? _____

3

Now go to the Progress Chart to record your score!   Total   30

Find the letter that will end the first word and start the second word.

Example   peac (<u>h</u>) ome

1 cor (___) rain

2 pe (___) ib

3 foo (___) hen

4 sea (___) ion

5 tow (___) ote

5

Underline two words, one from each group, that go together to form a new word. The word in the first group always comes first.

Example   (hand, <u>green</u>, for)   (light, <u>house</u>, sure)

6 (skin, jaw, front)   (spring, back, bone)

7 (bag, field, song)   (lark, pipes, hill)

8 (fort, flow, draw)   (bridge, road, water)

3

Add one letter to the word in capital letters to make a new word. The meaning of the new word is given in the clue.

Example   PLAN   simple   <u>plain</u>

9 FAST   a lot of food   _____

10 FAIL   not very strong   _____

11 PANT   something that grows in the garden   _____

12 LATE   something we use at meal times   _____

13 SIP   to fall   _____

14 PEAK   to talk   _____

15 RIGHT   to have a scare   _____

7

Find a word that is similar in meaning to the word in capital letters and that rhymes with the second word.

Example   CABLE   tyre   _wire_

16 INSTRUCT   peach   _____

17 GRAZE   hatch   _____

18 BROOK   dream   _____

19 RAIL CARRIAGES   stain   _____

20 SEASHORE   toast   _____   (5)

Complete the following expressions by underlining the missing word.

Example   Frog is to tadpole as swan is to (duckling, baby, cygnet).

21 Hoof is to horse as claw is to (zebra, cat, goat).

22 Flower is to garden as fish is to (stall, net, sea).

23 Cook is to stove as drive is to (bike, lane, car).

24 Croak is to frog as cluck is to (hen, owl, raven).

25 Plane is to sky as boat is to (float, sail, water).   (5)

If the code for ORANGE is LPXBQF, what are the codes for the following words?

26 NAG   _____

27 RAG   _____

28 ORE   _____

What do these codes stand for?

29 QFXP   _____

30 PXBQ   _____   (5)

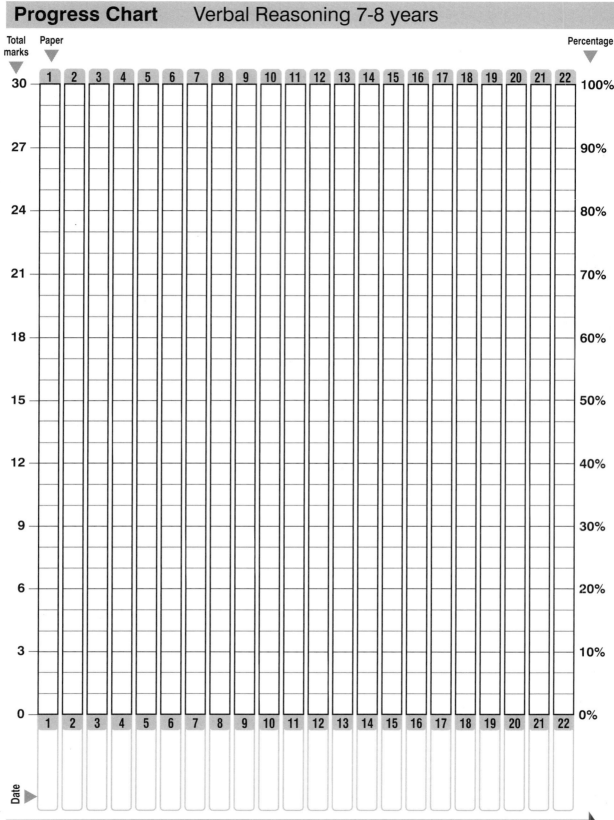

Progress Chart Verbal Reasoning 7-8 years

When you've finished the book read the Next Steps